John Donne
1572–1631

JOHN DONNE
(catalogue no. 125)

JOHN DONNE

 1572–1631

*A Catalogue of the
Anniversary Exhibition of
First and Early Editions
of His Works Held
at The Grolier Club*

February 15 to April 12, 1972

Compiled by
Robert S. Pirie

The Grolier Club

NEW YORK

TABLE OF CONTENTS

LIST OF ILLUSTRATIONS

FOREWORD

✻ ✻

It was appropriate that the Grolier Club, which sponsored, some seventy-five years ago, the first serious attempt at a scholarly edition of Donne's poems, should mark the four-hundredth anniversary of his birth by holding an exhibition in his honour.

The Grolier exhibition was remarkable in more ways than one. This catalogue bears witness to the learning and imagination that inspired the choice of the exhibits, and no one who was fortunate enough to be able actually to visit the exhibition will forget the visual impact made by their display. Ranged round the room, in most effective disposition, were copies of almost every one of the earliest editions of Donne's own writings, a selection of books that had belonged to him, books dedicated to him, books concerning him, presentation copies, autograph letters, manuscripts of his sermons and other works, together with intimate personal relics—the ring with his signet that belonged to Walton and copies of Walton's Lives, containing its impress, a portrait from the National Portrait Gallery in London, and, dominating the scene, a more than life-size—one is tempted to call it a more than death-size—photograph of the sepulchral monument in St. Paul's.

The exhibition was remarkable also in that its contents —apart from a few unique items—were drawn entirely from sources in the United States. In particular, it was a tour de force on the part of the organizers to have assembled so comprehensive an array without making a levy on the library of the *doyen* of Donne collectors, Sir Geoffrey

Keynes. Sir Geoffrey bestowed his blessing upon the enter-prise, and would no doubt himself have attended the open-ing day had he not been (as he said), at eighty-five, too old, and too busy, to cross the Atlantic for the purpose.

One of the projects occupying Sir Geoffrey was the preparation, for publication in the Quatercentenary year, of the fourth edition of his Bibliography. A glance through the three earlier editions—and in particular those sections devoted to Biography and Criticism—provokes reflection on the growth during the past half-century of interest in Donne on the part of scholars, collectors and the general public. That interest has become so extensive, and every corner in the field of Donne studies has been so thoroughly explored, that one wonders whether there is anything new for the critic to write about or for the bibliographer to chronicle: "John Donne: Dean Donne: all done!" one is tempted to exclaim. Students of "Eng. Lit.," however, are not so easily exhausted; they will make, if they cannot find, subjects for their articles and theses—Donne's medical imagery, Donne's legal metaphors, Donne's use of the preposition, a lost semicolon in his *Biathanatos*, the social background of his lyrics—lucubrations, however otiose, on themes such as these will continue to provide matter for the pages of his bibliographer.

This ever-growing enthusiasm for Donne is not so favor-able to the operations of the collector: "institutional" li-braries have absorbed so much, and private owners are so tenacious, that one might suppose that there is nothing left in the bookshops for the Donne collector to collect. Any such impression should be dispelled by the study of this catalogue, with its impressive list of rarities from the shelves of American collectors. How much the exhibition owed to their enthusiasm and expertise, to their prowess as collectors, and to their generosity as lenders, this catalogue makes plain.

JOHN SPARROW

All Souls College
October 3, 1972

COMPILER'S NOTE

❦ ❦

All exhibitions are primarily dependent for whatever success they may have on the generosity of various individuals and institutions and equally for whatever failings they may have on the organizer, but this exhibition more than any with which I have been associated possessed these qualities.

While the Grolier Club has always enjoyed excellent relations with the great libraries of England, their response on this occasion was far beyond what anyone could reasonably expect. Institutions such as the Cathedral Libraries of Lincoln and Salisbury, which are not in the habit of lending, sent valued possessions. As far as one can tell, the entire parish of Blunham, led by their rector Dr. Purchas, rallied behind the proposal to lend their magnificent communion cup presented to the parish by the great Dean himself. The Bodleian lent three superb manuscripts without which the exhibition would have lacked much of its excitement. It was a source of particular pleasure to exhibit for the first time in the United States a 17th century portrait of John Donne, cleaned and reframed for the occasion by the National Portrait Gallery, and to have on one shelf all four of the books dedicated to him. On this side of the Atlantic, Harvard opened wide its shelves as did Yale, the Pforzheimer Foundation and virtually every person asked.

In preparing this catalogue I have followed the format of the cards used at the exhibition, for which I drew heavily from the biography of Donne by the late Professor R. C. Bald. Titles have been substantially abbreviated, a convention which, while it may make the catalogue marginally less useful, is, I believe, more than offset by the availability of the great bibliography of John Donne by Sir Geoffrey Keynes, a fourth edition of which is shortly to be published by the Oxford University Press.

Since completeness was something of a goal, it is worth noting that only seven items by Donne printed before 1700 and listed in Keynes were not included in the exhibition (Keynes 11, 20, 25, 26a, 28, 35 and 74).

In closing, I would like to express my particular thanks to two close friends, John Sparrow, Warden of All Souls College, Oxford, who not only consented to interrupt a busy schedule and fly over to open the exhibition but lent generously from his own shelves and acted as custodian for all the loans from England, a mission not entirely free from anxiety; and William Stockhausen without whose generosity and enthusiasm this catalogue would not have seen the light of day.

ROBERT S. PIRIE

Hamilton, Massachusetts
July 20, 1972

LENDERS TO THE EXHIBITION

ROGER W. BARRETT
ABEL E. BERLAND
HERBERT T. F. CAHOON
ARTHUR A. HOUGHTON, JR.
DR. BENT JUEL-JENSEN
SIR GEOFFREY KEYNES
WILMARTH S. LEWIS
H. BRADLEY MARTIN
MR. AND MRS. ROBERT S. PIRIE
DR. CALVIN H. PLIMPTON
DR. GORDON N. RAY
JOHN SPARROW
WILLIAM E. STOCKHAUSEN
ROBERT H. TAYLOR
MR. AND MRS. ARTHUR E. VERSHBOW
THEODORE YONGE
THE BODLEIAN LIBRARY
THE RECTOR AND CHURCHWARDENS OF THE
BLUNHAM PARISH CHURCH, BEDFORDSHIRE
CAMBRIDGE UNIVERSITY LIBRARY
THE GROLIER CLUB
THE HARVARD COLLEGE LIBRARY
KING'S COLLEGE, CAMBRIDGE
LINCOLN CATHEDRAL LIBRARY, BY PERMISSION OF
THE DEAN AND CHAPTER
THE MASSACHUSETTS HISTORICAL SOCIETY

THE PIERPONT MORGAN LIBRARY
NATIONAL PORTRAIT GALLERY, LONDON
THE NEWBERRY LIBRARY
THE OSBORN COLLECTION, YALE UNIVERSITY LIBRARY
THE CARL H. PFORZHEIMER LIBRARY
THE PHILIP H. AND A.S.W. ROSENBACH FOUNDATION
SALISBURY CATHEDRAL LIBRARY, BY PERMISSION OF
THE DEAN AND CHAPTER
YALE UNIVERSITY LIBRARY
DAWSON'S OF PALL MALL
B. WEINREB LTD.
ANONYMOUS

Catalogue

❀ PROSE WORKS ❀

DONNE, JOHN
1 *Pseudo-Martyr*, London, 1610.
Contemporary vellum. STC 7048, Keynes 1.

Although Donne is known to have presented copies to various important people, this one to Rowland Woodward and the one to Lord Ellesmere (see item 34) are the only two unquestionable ones to have survived.

Lent by John Sparrow, Esq.

2 Another copy
Contemporary vellum.

This copy belonged at one time to Sir Heneage Finch, Recorder of London and Speaker of the House of Commons. That Donne knew Finch at least by 1622 is clear since they were both made honorary members of the Council of the Virginia Company on 3 July of that year. It is not unreasonable to suppose that they had known each other for some time. Both from the similarity of its binding and the fact that the errata are corrected in manuscript in a hand similar to that used in the presentation copy to Lord Ellesmere, it is possible to conclude that this also was a presentation copy from the author.

Lent by the Carl H. Pforzheimer Library.

2a Another copy
See item 34.

FITZHERBERT, THOMAS
3 *A supplement to the discussion of M. D. Barlowes answere*,
n.p., 1613.
Contemporary vellum. STC 11021.

Fitzherbert, later to become rector of the English College at Rome, attempted here to answer *Pseudo-Martyr* by discrediting Donne whom he describes as having "belched out so many lucianicall, impious, blasphemous, and Atheistical jests" that they would make the Prophet stagger.

Lent by the Harvard College Library.

3

DONNE, JOHN

4 *Conclave Ignati*, London, 1611.

Modern morocco. STC 7026, Keynes 2.

A remarkable copy of the first edition of Donne's second book, completely uncut.

Lent by the Yale University Library.

DONNE, JOHN

5 *Conclave Ignati*, [?Hanau, 1611].

Contemporary vellum. Keynes 3.

The assumption that this second edition was printed in Hanau is based on the fact that two of the five recorded copies are bound up with other tracts printed there.

Lent by the Cambridge University Library.

DONNE, JOHN

6 *Ignatius His Conclave*, London, 1611.

Modern morocco. STC 7027, Keynes 4.

Of this, the first edition in english, only eight copies are recorded.

Lent by the Harvard College Library.

DONNE, JOHN

7 *Ignatius His Conclave*, London, 1626.

19th century calf. STC 7028, Keynes 7.

Like its predecessors, this fourth edition, the second in english, is exceedingly rare, only four copies being recorded.

Lent by the Cambridge University Library.

DONNE, JOHN

8 *Ignatius His Conclave*, London, 1634.

19th century calf. STC 7029, Keynes 8.

This edition and the one of 1635 are relatively common, eleven and fifteen copies respectively being recorded.

Lent by Mr. and Mrs. Robert S. Pirie.

DONNE, JOHN

9 *Ignatius His Conclave*, London, 1635.

Modern three-quarter morocco. STC 7030, Keynes 9.

Lent by Mr. and Mrs. Robert S. Pirie.

DONNE, JOHN

10 *Biathanatos*. Contemporary manuscript, ca. 1615.

Contemporary calf.

This manuscript in a scribal hand with marginal corrections by Donne contains as well an autograph letter by him presenting it to Sir Edward Herbert, later Lord Herbert of Cherbury, who gave it to the Bodleian Library in 1642.

Lent by the Bodleian Library.

DONNE, JOHN

11 *Biathanatos*, London [1647?].

Contemporary calf. Wing D1858, Keynes 47.

Presentation copy from John Donne, Jr., to William Hodges.

At least a dozen presentation copies are known and the four I have examined are all on special (large) paper in identical bindings. In sending a manuscript of it to Sir Robert Ker in 1619 Donne wrote: "Let any that your discretion admits to the sight of it, know the date of it; and that it is a Book written by Jack Donne, and not by D. Donne."

The Heber–Britwell–Jerome Kern copy.

Lent by Mr. and Mrs. Robert S. Pirie.

DONNE, JOHN

12 Another copy

Contemporary calf. Wing D1858, Keynes 47.

The presentation inscription to the Earl of Denbigh is most interesting, not only because it helps to ascertain the publication date, but because it indicates that there was some controversy surrounding publication, which Donne's son attempted to forestall by seeking important patrons. The book is in fact dedicated to Lord Philip Herbert.

Lent by the Harvard College Library.

5

DONNE, JOHN

13 *Biathanatos*, London, 1648.
Contemporary calf. Wing D1859, Keynes 48.
A reissue with the same sheets as Keynes 47 but having a cancel title.
The Harmsworth copy.
Lent by Mr. and Mrs. Robert S. Pirie.

DONNE, JOHN

14 *Biathanatos*, London, 1700.
Contemporary sheep. Wing D1860, Keynes 49.
Horace Walpole's copy of the second edition with his bookplate.
Lent by Wilmarth S. Lewis, Esq.

Although the publication in 1647 of *Biathanatos* did not give rise to any immediate replies, at least two were written before 1700 and copies of both of them were shown.

DENNY, SIR WILLIAM

15 *Pelecanicidium, or the Christian adviser Against Self-Murder*, London, 1653.
Contemporary black morocco. Wing D1051.
The Farmer–Britwell copy.
Lent anonymously.

PIERCE, EZRA

16 *A Discourse of Self-Murder*, London, 1692.
Modern wrappers. Wing P2162.
Lent by the Yale University Library.

DONNE, JOHN

17 *Devotions Upon Emergent Occasions*, London, 1624.
Contemporary vellum. STC 7033, Keynes 34.
This is undoubtedly the finest copy known of the first edition of Donne's best-known prose work.
Lent by Robert H. Taylor, Esq.

DONNE, JOHN

18 *Devotions Upon Emergent Occasions*, London, 1624.
Contemporary vellum gilt. STC 7034, Keynes 36.

The binding on this copy of the second edition is similar to ones in the travelling libraries of Sir Francis Bacon (Toledo Museum of Art), Lord Egerton (Huntington Library), Sir Julius Caesar (British Museum), and one made for a member of the Madden family (Brotherton Library, Leeds). The books, each with a gilt angel stamped on the sides, as in the present example, were divided into classes such as Poetry, History, etc., identifiable by the color of the ties.

The Jennings–Cherry Garrard copy.

Lent by Mr. and Mrs. Robert S. Pirie.

DONNE, JOHN

19 *Devotions Upon Emergent Occasions*, London, 1626.
Contemporary calf. STC 7035, Keynes 37.

In this, the first issue of the third edition, the title page is dated 1626 but the colophon bears the correct date of 1627.

Lent by John Sparrow, Esq.

DONNE, JOHN

20 *Devotions Upon Emergent Occasions*, London, 1627.
Contemporary calf (Oxford binding?). STC 7035a,
Keynes 38.

In this issue the date on the title page has been changed to 1627 conforming it with the date in the colophon.

Lent by Mr. and Mrs. Robert S. Pirie.

DONNE, JOHN

21 *Devotions Upon Emergent Occasions*, London, 1634.
Contemporary calf. STC 7036, Keynes 39.

The first pocket edition and the first to contain the extraordinary frontispiece based on the effigy of Donne erected at St. Paul's Cathedral on 30 November 1632.

Lent by John Sparrow, Esq.

7

DONNE, JOHN

22 *Devotions Upon Emergent Occasions*, London, 1638.
Contemporary calf. STC 7037, Keynes 40.

Like the preceding, copies of this edition are exceedingly scarce. Of the seven recorded copies four, including this one, lack the frontispiece.
Lent by Mr. and Mrs. Robert S. Pirie.

DONNE, JOHN

23 *Essayes in Divinity*, London, 1651.
19th century russia. Wing D1861, Keynes 50.

This is one of five recorded copies with the dedication to Sir Henry Vane, Junior uncancelled.
The Lefferts copy.
Lent by H. Bradley Martin, Esq.

DONNE, JOHN

24 *Essays in Divinity*, London, 1651.
Modern sprinkled calf. Wing D1861, Keynes 50.

This copy from the J. C. Lynn angling collection at one time belonged to Donne's biographer Izaak Walton and contains various marginalia in his hand. As is usually the case, it lacks the dedication.
Lent by Mr. and Mrs. Robert S. Pirie.

DONNE, JOHN

25 *Problems Not Printed.* Manuscript ca. 1630.
Contemporary calf.

No doubt because of their witty and mildly licentious nature contemporary manuscripts of the *Juvenilia* are not uncommon although few are in private hands.
Bound with copies of the first editions of the *Poems* and *Juvenilia*.
Lent by Abel E. Berland, Esq.

DONNE, JOHN

26 *Ivvenilia: or Certaine Paradoxes, and Problemes*, London, 1633.
Contemporary vellum gilt. STC 7043, Keynes 43.

Donne said that these trifles "were made rather to deceave tyme then her daughter truth" and, in fact, because of their nature they were not published during his lifetime. Copies of both this and the second edition are frequently found bound with the 1633 edition of Donne's poems, but copies bound separately in contemporary bindings are very rare.

Lent by Mr. and Mrs. Robert S. Pirie.

DONNE, JOHN

27 *Ivvenilia or Certaine Paradoxes and Problemes*, London, 1633.

Modern calf. STC 7044, Keynes 44.

This second edition was issued without license and, perhaps for that reason, is considerably scarcer than the first.

Lent by Mr. and Mrs. Robert S. Pirie.

DONNE, JOHN

28 *Paradoxes, Problems, Essayes, Characters*, London, 1652.

Contemporary calf. Wing D1867, Keynes 46.

Bound with the 1651 edition of Donne's *Essayes in Divinity*.
The Tollemache copy.
Lent by Mr. and Mrs. Robert S. Pirie.

DONNE, JOHN

29 *Paradoxes, Problems, Essayes, Characters*, London, 1652.

Contemporary calf. Wing D1866, Keynes 45.

Although previously this was considered to be the first issue of this edition, it is almost certain that it is the second, a fact indicated by the removal of certain parts of the dedication. As is frequently the case, this copy is bound with the 1651 edition of Donne's *Essayes in Divinity*.

The Sheppard–Jennings–Cherry Garrard copy.
Lent by Mr. and Mrs. Robert S. Pirie.

DUNTON, JOHN

30 *Athenian Sport*, London, 1707.

19th century boards. Keynes 46a.

Eight of Donne's paradoxes are reprinted here without acknowledgement.

Lent by Mr. and Mrs. Robert S. Pirie.

9

OVERBURY, SIR THOMAS

31 *A Wife, Now the Widow of Sir Tho. Overburye*, London, 1614.

Modern morocco. STC 18905, Keynes 73.

This is the first appearance in print of Donne's "Newes from the very Country." No copies of the first edition, three of the second and four of this third edition are recorded.

Lent by Mr. and Mrs. Robert S. Pirie.

OVERBURY, SIR THOMAS

32 *Sir Thomas Overbury His Wife*, London, 1622.

Contemporary vellum. STC 18913, Keynes 73a.

In this edition two additional works of Donne's, *The True Character of a Dunce* and *An Essay of Valour*, appeared for the first time.

Lent by Mr. and Mrs. Robert S. Pirie.

HOWELL, JAMES

33 *Cottoni Posthuma*, London, 1651.

Contemporary calf. Wing c6485.

Although attributed here to Sir Philip Sidney, this, in fact, is the second appearance of Donne's *Valour Anatomized in a Fancie*, the first being in the 1622 edition of Overbury's *Wife*.

Lent by Mr. and Mrs. Robert S. Pirie.

LETTERS

DONNE, JOHN

34 *Pseudo-Martyr*, London, 1610.

Contemporary vellum. STC 7048, Keynes 1.

Pinned in the back is an a.l.s. presenting this copy to Lord Chancellor Ellesmere who had employed Donne as a secretary from 1596 to 1601. The reference in the last line to his lordship's having "longe since pardoned greater faults in mee" undoubtedly refers to Donne's elopement with the daughter of Sir George More while in the Lord Chancellor's employ. Sealed with Donne's "sheaf of snakes" seal.

The Bridgewater copy.

Lent by Mr. and Mrs. Robert S. Pirie.

DONNE, JOHN
35 A.L.S. to Sir Henry Martin, 9 May 1622.

This letter sheds an interesting light on the practice of transferring benefices in the 17th century. Donne had promised to resign the living of Keyston to John Scott upon a "better preferment," and, based on the Earl of Buckingham's representations that he had the living of Salisbury, he did so. In fact, it turned out he was not to get Salisbury, but in the meantime Henry Seyliard had been presented with Keyston by the Archbishop of Canterbury. Donne brought suit in the Court of Delegates to quash the claim of Seyliard, and a panel, including Sir Henry Martin, the addressee of this letter, was appointed to hear it. In the end Scott received the living. On the reverse Martin has written a draft of his report on the case. Sealed with Donne's "Christ crucified on an anchor" seal.
Lent by the Harvard College Library.

DONNE, JOHN
36 A.L.S. to Sir Nicholas Carey, 23 July 1624.

Donne was evidently the host at some feast for which he needed a deer and so having borrowed it from his close friend, Sir John Danvers, he hoped to repay the loan with one from his brother-in-law, Sir Nicholas. That he was successful is clear from a letter of 1 September 1624 in which he offers to repay Sir Nicholas with a deer from the park at Knole belonging to his patron, the Earl of Dorset. Donne was quite extravagant in the quality of the letter paper he used. Two of the examples shown, this being one, have gilded edges, a most unusual touch at this period.
From the Alfred Morrison collection.
Lent by the Carl H. Pforzheimer Library.

DONNE, JOHN
37 A.L.S. to Sir Nicholas Carey, 21 June 1625.

In this letter to his close friend and brother-in-law, Donne talks about his recent ill-health and tells of arrangements to go to Chelsea to stay with the Danvers family to complete his recovery. In this letter he once more asks for the gift of a deer, a favor he had promised not to request again. Sealed with Donne's "sheaf of snakes" seal, a very late instance of its use.
Lent by the Harvard College Library.

DONNE, JOHN
38 Contemporary Transcript of Two Letters.

This leaf and its conjugate, believed to be in the possession of Miss Mary

Donne of Chester, England, were at one time in the Anderdon and O'Flahertie collections. It preserves the text of two of Donne's letters which were
not printed until the appearance of Sir Edmund Gosse's *Life and Letters of
John Donne*, London, 1899.
Lent by Roger W. Barrett, Esq.

DONNE, JOHN
39 *Letters to Severall Persons of Honour*, London, 1651.
Contemporary calf gilt. Wing D1864, Keynes 55.
This is one of five recorded copies of the first edition on special (large)
paper.
The Buxton Forman–Litchfield copy.
Lent by Mr. and Mrs. Robert S. Pirie.

39a Another copy
See item 129.

DONNE, JOHN
40 *Letters to Severall Persons of Honour*, London, 1654.
Contemporary sheep. Wing D1865, Keynes 56.
This copy of the second issue belonged to the second Lord Herbert of
Cherbury at whose wedding on 19 November 1627 to Lady Mary Egerton
Donne preached the marriage sermon.
Lent by Mr. and Mrs. Robert S. Pirie.

41 *Cabala, Mysteries of State*, London, 1654.
Contemporary calf. Wing C184, Keynes 57.
This interesting collection of letters by the great and near great of
the period includes two by Donne to his patron the Duke of Buckingham.
Lent by Mr. and Mrs. Robert S. Pirie.

DONNE, JOHN JR., editor
42 *A Collection Of Letters, Made By Sr Tobie Mathews K^t*,
London, 1660.
Contemporary calf. Wing M1319, Keynes 59.
This collection contains thirty-eight of Donne's letters.
The Britwell–J.P.R. Lyell copy.
Lent by Mr. and Mrs. Robert S. Pirie.

Donne, John Jr., editor

43 *A collection of letters Made By Sr Tobie Mathews, Kt.,*
London, 1692.
Contemporary sheep. Wing M1321, Keynes 62.

A rare reissue of the 1660 edition with a cancel title. This copy is particularly interesting because of the contemporary notes identifying various
of the personages mentioned in the text.
Lent by the Harvard College Library.

Walton, Izaak

44 *The Life of Mr. George Herbert,* London, 1670.
Contemporary sheep. Wing w669, Keynes 60.

Four letters of Donne to Herbert's mother appear here.
Lent by Mr. and Mrs. Robert S. Pirie.

SERMONS

Donne, John

45 Sermons. Manuscript ca. 1630.
Contemporary calf gilt.

This magnificent manuscript is the most complete of all such collections,
containing the text of sixteen of Donne's sermons. No other manuscript contains the text of a sermon not included here.
From the Wilfred Merton collection. (See illustration facing page 16.)
Lent by the Bodleian Library.

Donne, John

46 *A Sermon Upon The XV. Verse Of The XX. Chapter Of
The Booke Of Judges,* London, 1622.
Contemporary vellum. STC 7053, Keynes 12.

This copy of the first issue of the first of Donne's sermons to appear in
print is bound with two anti-Catholic works of the period.
Lent by Mr. and Mrs. Robert S. Pirie.

DONNE, JOHN

47 *A Sermon Upon The XV. Verse Of The XX. Chapter Of The Book Of Judges*, London, 1622.
19th century boards. STC 7053, Keynes 13.

In this issue four of the errata have been corrected, but the glaring one on the title page—that this is in fact a sermon on the XX verse of the V chapter of the Book of Judges—was not corrected until the next.

Lent by John Sparrow, Esq.

DONNE, JOHN

48 *A Sermon Upon The XX. Verse Of The V. Chapter Of The Book Of Judges*, London, 1622.
Contemporary calf. STC 7054, Keynes 14.

Bound with:

DONNE, JOHN, *Six Sermons*, Cambridge, 1634. STC 7056, Keynes 27.
DONNE, JOHN, *Encaenia*, London, 1623. STC 7039, Keynes 16.
DONNE, JOHN, *A Sermon Preached to the Kings Mtie At Whitehall*, London, 1626. STC 7050, Keynes 21.
DONNE, JOHN, *The First Sermon Preached to King Charles*, London, 1625. STC 7040, Keynes 19.
And five other contemporary sermons.

Lent by Mr. and Mrs. Robert S. Pirie.

DONNE, JOHN

49 *A Sermon Upon The VIII. Verse Of The I. Chapter Of The Acts Of The Apostles*, London, 1622.
19th century half calf. STC 7051, Keynes 15.

This is the rare first edition of Donne's sermon to the Virginia Company. Some three or four hundred people were present when it was delivered and later at the feast in Merchant Taylors' Hall which followed, though Chamberlain said that "many of the nobilitie and counsaile were invited but few came." This has been described as "the first missionary sermon," although, in fact, Donne was not the first to urge the Company to convert the natives.

The O'Flahertie copy.

Lent by the Yale University Library.

DONNE, JOHN

50 *Encaenia*, London, 1623.

Half morocco. STC 7039, Keynes 16.

This sermon was specially commissioned and printed at the request of the Masters of the Bench to whom it is dedicated.

The Hagen–Clawson copy.

Lent by the Carl H. Pforzheimer Library.

DONNE, JOHN

51 *A Sermon Upon the Eighth Verse of the First Chapter of the Acts of the Apostles*, London, 1624.

Modern morocco. STC 7052, Keynes 18.

In this second edition of Donne's sermon to the Virginia Company the errata have been corrected. Most of the recorded copies appear bound up as part of the *Foure Sermons* or the *Five Sermons*.

Lent by the Harvard College Library.

DONNE, JOHN

52 *The First Sermon Preached to King Charles, At Saint James*, London, 1625.

19th century boards. STC 7040, Keynes 19.

A contemporary letter-writer relates that on 3 April 1625 Charles left his private chambers for the first time since the death of his father on 27 March "and then dined abroad, in the privy-chamber, being in a plain black cloth cloak to the ancle; and so went after dinner into the chapel, Dr. Donne preaching, Lord Davers carrying the sword before him, his majesty looking very pale, his visage being the true glass of his inward, as well as his accoutrements of external mourning."

Lent by Mr. and Mrs. Robert S. Pirie.

DONNE, JOHN

53 *A Sermon, Preached To The Kings Mtie*, London, 1626.

Modern morocco. STC 7050, Keynes 21.

Only one other uncut copy is recorded of any of Donne's sermons.

The Hagen–Clawson copy.

Lent by the Carl H. Pforzheimer Library.

DONNE, JOHN

54 *A Sermon Of Commemoration Of The Lady Danvers, late Wife of Sr. John Danvers*, London, 1627.

Contemporary calf gilt. STC 7049, Keynes 23.

By reason of its scarcity and because it is not included in any of the early collected editions of Donne's sermons, it is believed that the printing of this funeral sermon was arranged for by Lady Danvers' family, particularly her son George Herbert, a number of whose poems are included. Izaak Walton heard Donne preach this sermon, and it was the only occasion on which he saw Herbert, whose biography he later wrote.

Lent by Mr. and Mrs. Robert S. Pirie.

DONNE, JOHN

55 *Deaths Duell*, London, 1632.

Modern calf. STC 7031, Keynes 24.

This sermon was preached by Donne just five weeks before his death and plans for its publication were among his last activities.

Lent by H. Bradley Martin, Esq.

DONNE, JOHN

56 *Deaths Duell*, London, 1633.

Modern three-quarter morocco. STC 7032, Keynes 26.

The second edition.

The Vanston copy.

Lent by Mr. and Mrs. Robert S. Pirie.

MILBOURNE, WILLIAM, editor

57 *Wisdome Crying Out to Sinners*, London, 1639.

Contemporary calf. STC 17920, Keynes 28a.

Not much is known of the editor of this rare little volume other than that he was curate of Brancepeth near Durham. Only four copies are recorded of the first issue and only four of this, the second.

The third sermon, "of Mans timely remembring of his Creator," the only one by Donne in the volume, was reprinted with the text greatly altered in *XXVI Sermons*, 1660.

Lent by the Cambridge University Library.

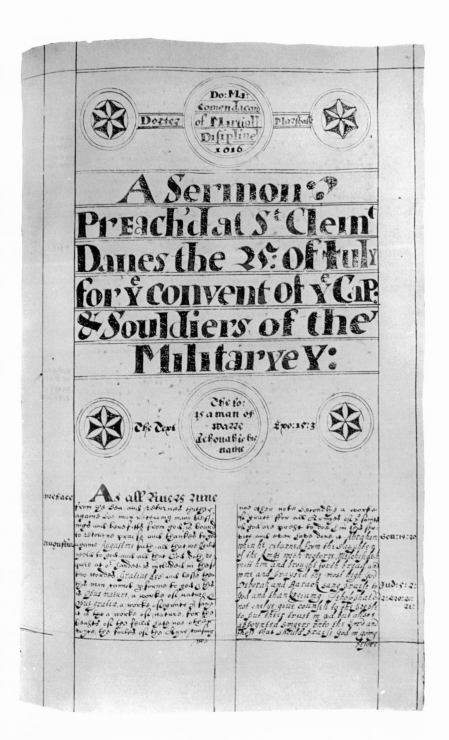

THE WILFRED MERTON MANUSCRIPT OF DONNE'S SERMONS
(catalogue no. 45)

THE BLUNHAM COMMUNION CUP AND PATEN
(catalogue no. 154)

THE BLUNHAM COMMUNION CUP, bottom view
(catalogue no. 154)

THE
LAWYERS
PHILOSOPHY:
OR,
LAVV BROVGHT
TO LIGHT.

Poetized
In a Diuine Rhapfodie or
Contemplatiue Poem.
BY
ROGER TISDALE, *Gent.*

Sat Serò.

At London printed for *I. T.* and *H. G.* and
are to bee fold at the Widdow *Goſſons* in
Pannier Alley. 1622.

THE
BARREN
TREE.
A
Sermon Preached at *Pauls* Croſſe
October 26. 1623.

BY
THO: ADAMS.

LONDON,
Printed by AVG: MATHEVVES for
IOHN GRISMAND, and are to be fold
at his Shop in *Pauls* Alley, at the figne
of the Gunne. 1623.

THE
ROYALL
RECEIPT:
OR,
HEZEKIAHS
PHYSICKE.

A SERMON DELIVERED
At PAVLS-Croſſe, on MICHA-
ELMAS Day, 1622.

By ELIAS PETLEY.

DEVT. 30. 19.
——— *Behold, I haue fet before you Death and Life,
therefore chufe Life.* ———

LONDON,
Printed by B. A. for EDWARD BLACKMORE, and
are to be fold at his Shop, at the great South
Doore, going vp into S. PAVLES.
1623.

A
SVB-POENA
FROM THE STAR-
CHAMBER OF
HEAVEN.

A Sermon preached at Pauls Croſſe
the 4. of Auguſt. 1622.

With ſome particular Enlargements
*which the limited time would
not then allow.*

By DAN. DONNE, Maſter of Arts, and
Miniſter of the Word.

Auguſt. Confeſſ. lib. 8 cap. 12.
Tolle, Lege: Tolle, Lege.

LONDON,
Printed by *Auguſtine Mathewes* for *John
Griſmand,* and are to be fold at his Shop
in *Pauls* Alley at the Signe of
the Gunne. 1623.

BOOKS DEDICATED TO JOHN DONNE
(catalogue nos. 108–111)

DONNE, JOHN

58 *Three Sermons Upon Speciall Occasions*, London, 1623.
Modern calf. STC 7057, Keynes 17.

One of two known copies of the first issue of the first attempt at publishing a collection of Donne's sermons.
Lent by the Massachusetts Historical Society.

DONNE, JOHN

59 *Three Sermons Upon Speciall Occasions*, London, 1624.
Contemporary calf. STC 7057.5, Keynes 17a.

Aside from a fragment at Trinity College, Cambridge, this is the only copy known of the second issue of the first attempt at a collected edition of Donne's sermons.
Bound with:
    DONNE, JOHN, *Six Sermons*, Cambridge, 1634. STC 7056, Keynes 27.
    DONNE, JOHN, *Deaths Duell*, London, 1633. STC 7032, Keynes 26.
Lent by Mr. and Mrs. Robert S. Pirie.

DONNE, JOHN

60 *Five Sermons Upon Speciall Occasions*, London, 1626.
Contemporary vellum. STC 7041, Keynes 22.

This, the third collection of Donne's sermons to be issued, is relatively common; at least twelve other copies are recorded.
Lent by The Rosenbach Foundation.

DONNE, JOHN

61 *Six Sermons Upon Severall Occasions*, Cambridge, 1634.
Modern vellum. STC 7056, Keynes 27.

This fourth collection of Donne's sermons differs from the earlier attempts in being completely reset and not simply made up from the unsold sheets of sermons which had been issued separately.
Lent by H. Bradley Martin, Esq.

DONNE, JOHN

62 *LXXX Sermons Preached By That Learned And Reverend Divine*, London, 1640.
Contemporary black morocco. STC 7038, Keynes 29.

This, the first of a projected two-volume edition of Donne's sermons (a

17

third volume was printed much later) was prepared for the press by John Donne, Jr., at the behest of Charles I. This copy has the engraved title in the second state.

Lent by Mr. and Mrs. Robert S. Pirie.

63 Another copy
19th century three-quarter calf.

This copy, in addition to belonging to Wordsworth, is one of those books borrowed by Coleridge and returned immeasurably enriched by his marginalia.

The Johnson–Wordsworth–Loft–Vores–Marshall–Corliss Lamont–John Livingston Lowes copy.

Lent by the Harvard College Library.

63a Another copy
See item 131.

DONNE, JOHN

64 *Fifty Sermons, Preached By That Learned And Reverend Divine*, London, 1649.
Contemporary calf. Wing D1862, Keynes 30.

Although entered in the Stationer's Register on 19 February 1639/40, and again in 1644 when the text was actually ready, Donne delayed the publication of this second volume of his father's sermons, apparently for fear of persecution from the Commonwealth government.

The Sheppard–Whibley copy.

Lent by Mr. and Mrs. Robert S. Pirie.

DONNE, JOHN

65 *XXVI. Sermons Preached By That Learned and Reverend Divine*, London, 1660/10.
Contemporary calf. Wing D1872, Keynes 31.

This last volume of Donne's sermons was prepared for the press and printed at the expense of his son not long before his death. In a postscript to the preface he states that only five hundred copies were printed, "which will somewhat advance the Price." All in all it is a careless bit of work, containing, in fact, only twenty-three sermons.

Lent by Mr. and Mrs. Robert S. Pirie.

DONNE, JOHN

66 *XXVI. Sermons (Never Before Publish'd) Preached By
That Learned and Reverend Divine,* London, 1661.
Contemporary calf. Wing D1873, Keynes 32.
A variant issue with a cancel title.
The Chirk Castle copy.
Lent by Mr. and Mrs. Robert S. Pirie.

DONNE, JOHN

67 *XXVI. Sermons Preached By That Learned and Reverend
Divine,* London, 1661.
19th century calf. Wing D1874, Keynes 32A.
This is the rarest of the three issues of *XXVI Sermons,* only five copies
being recorded, and the imprint offers some clue as to the reason. Several
copies, including this one, are known with the title page defaced to remove
the words "The Third Volume," which can perhaps be explained by the
twelve years intervening between the publication of this and the preceding
volume, and the change in booksellers through whom it was distributed.
Lent by Mr. and Mrs. Robert S. Pirie.

 POETRY

DONNE, JOHN

68 A Letter to the Lady Carey, and Mrs. Essex Riche.
Autograph manuscript, ca. 1611–12.
Apart from two Latin epigrams, one of two and the other of four lines,
this is the only poetical manuscript in Donne's hand known to exist. It lay
unrecognized in the papers of the Dukes of Manchester until 1970 when it
was sold at auction. The two sisters Donne addresses in this poem were
daughters of Robert Rich, first Earl of Warwick, and that this is the copy
actually sent to them by Donne is clear from the manner in which it is folded
and addressed. The text contains significant variations from all printed texts
and sheds important light on his technique as a poet.
Lent by the Bodleian Library.

DONNE, JOHN

69 *Poems*, ca. 1620.

Contemporary vellum. Keynes K.

An important contemporary manuscript, one of about twenty which present a more or less complete text of the canon of Donne's poetry.

Lent by The Osborn Collection, Yale University Library.

DONNE, JOHN

70 *Poems*, ca. 1620.

19th century morocco. Not in Keynes.

This little volume contains eighty poems which are definitely by Donne, five doubtful ones, and twenty-two others by Beaumont, Corbet, Raleigh, Wotton, and others. It is of some textual significance as well as being an attractive example of the format in which Donne's poems became familiar to his contemporaries.

Lent by the Harvard College Library.

DONNE, JOHN

71 *Poems*, ca. 1620.

19th century russia. Not in Keynes.

This manuscript contains about a hundred songs and elegies, two divine poems, five satires, fifteen problems, and nine paradoxes. Like all such manuscripts it contains several interesting variations from the printed texts.

Lent by The Osborn Collection, Yale University Library.

JONSON, BEN

72 *Volpone Or The Foxe*, London, 1607.

Modern morocco. STC 14783, Keynes 69.

In addition to its importance as a work of Jonson's, this volume contains Donne's first appearance in print.

Lent by Mr. and Mrs. Robert S. Pirie.

WYBARNE, JOSEPH

73 *The New Age of Old Names*, London, 1609.

Modern morocco. STC 26055.

This interesting book contains references to Marlowe's *Tamberlane*, Sidney's *Arcadia*, and various references to Spenser. In addition it is Donne's second appearance in print, the first appearance in print of any portion of his *Satyres*, and contains in the fourth line thereof an otherwise unrecorded variant reading.

Lent by Mr. and Mrs. Robert S. Pirie.

CORYAT, THOMAS
74 *Coryat's Crudities*, London, 1611.
Contemporary calf. STC 5808, Keynes 70.

Coryat, Christopher Brooke, Inigo Jones, Donne, and other literary figures of the day belonged to a club which met occasionally at the Mermaid Tavern, and all but three of the members supplied puffing verses for this rather dull book.

Lent by Mr. and Mrs. Robert S. Pirie.

CORYAT, THOMAS
75 *The Odcombian Banquet*. London, 1611.
Modern half morocco. STC 5810, Keynes 70a.

The general amusement over the quantity and tenor of the puffing verses in Coryat's *Crudities* resulted in their being published as a separate volume.

Lent by Dr. Bent Juel-Jensen.

DONNE, JOHN
76 *The First Anniversarie. An anatomie of the World*, London, 1612.
The Second Anniversarie. Of The Progres of the Soule, London, 1612.
Contemporary vellum. STC 7023, Keynes 75.

This, the second edition of *The First Anniversarie* and the first edition of *The Second Anniversarie*, is known by only seven copies, two of which are incomplete.

The Richard Farmer copy.
Lent by Mr. and Mrs. Robert S. Pirie.

DONNE, JOHN
77 *The First Anniversarie*, London, 1621.
The second Anniversarie, London, 1621.

18th century calf. STC 7024, Keynes 76.

The third edition of *The First Anniversarie* and second edition of *The second Anniversarie*. Only four copies are recorded.
The Edmund Gosse copy.
Lent by the Harvard College Library.

DONNE, JOHN
78 *An Anatomie Of The World*, London, 1625.
Of The Progress of The Soule, London, 1625.
Uncut, stitched as issued. STC 7025, Keynes 77.

The fourth and last separate edition of Donne's Anniversaries, of which seven copies are recorded, three, including this, incomplete.
Lent by Mr. and Mrs. Robert S. Pirie.

SYLVESTER, JOSHUA
79 *Lachrymae Lachrymarum or the Spirit of Teares Distilled*, London, 1613.
Modern morocco. STC 23578, Keynes 72.

Donne's elegy first appeared in this third edition of Sylvester's collection of verses on the death of Prince Henry. Ben Jonson said that Donne told him that "he wrott that Epitaph on Prince Henry . . . to match Sir Ed. Herbert in obscurenesse," and he appears to have succeeded.
Lent by Mr. and Mrs. Robert S. Pirie.

80 *A Helpe to Memorie and Discourse*, London, 1630.
19th century calf. STC 1551.6, Keynes 73b.

This early appearance of Donne's "The Broken Heart" and his famous song "Go and Catch a Falling Starre" was discovered by James Walsh of the Houghton Library in 1956. Only five copies are recorded.
Lent by the Harvard College Library.

DONNE, JOHN
81 *Poems*, London, 1633.
Contemporary morocco. STC 7045, Keynes 78.

The first collected edition of Donne's poems, derived according to current scholarly thinking from manuscript sources in direct descent from the author's papers. It has been the basis of all scholarly editions since then, including the Grolier Club edition of 1895. Only two copies in contemporary morocco are recorded.

The Metcalfe–Terry copy.
Lent by Arthur A. Houghton, Esq.

DONNE, JOHN
82 Another copy
Contemporary vellum.

This copy was opened to the first appearance in print of "A Letter to the Lady Carey, and Mrs. Essex Riche From Amyens" for the manuscript of which see item 68.

The Jennings?–Litchfield copy.
Lent by Robert H. Taylor, Esq.

82a Another copy
See item 91.

DONNE, JOHN
83 *Poems*, London, 1635.
Contemporary sheep. STC 7046, Keynes 79.

This second edition contains seventeen additional poems by Donne and is the first to have the portrait.

The Jennings copy.
Lent by Mr. and Mrs. Robert S. Pirie.

83a Another copy
See item 127.

DONNE, JOHN
84 *Poems*, London, 1639.
Contemporary calf. STC 7047, Keynes 80.

This is a reissue of the second edition with the errata corrected and some minor additions.

The Jennings copy.
Lent by Mr. and Mrs. Robert S. Pirie.

DONNE, JOHN
85 *Poems*, London, 1649.
Contemporary calf. Wing D1868, Keynes 81.

This edition, containing only two new poems, is the rarest of the 17th century printings of Donne's *Poems*, only six copies being recorded.
Presented by Sarah Orne Jewett to Charles Eliot Norton.
Lent by the Harvard College Library.

DONNE, JOHN
86 *Poems*, London, 1650.
Contemporary calf. Wing D1869, Keynes 82.

This is a reissue of the 1649 edition with a new first quire and additional material added at the end.
Lent by Mr. and Mrs. Robert S. Pirie.

DONNE, JOHN
87 *Poems*, London, 1654.
Contemporary sheep. Wing D1870, Keynes 83.

This is a reissue of the 1650 issue with a new title.
The Jennings–Hayward copy.
Lent by Mr. and Mrs. Robert S. Pirie.

87a Another copy
See item 92.

DONNE, JOHN
88 *Poems, &c.*, London, 1669.
Contemporary morocco. Wing D1871, Keynes 84.

This appears to be the dedication copy, as it has the bookplate of Fulwer Craven, whose ancestor, William, Lord Craven, was the dedicatee.
Lent by Mr. and Mrs. Robert S. Pirie.

DONNE, JOHN
89 Another copy
Contemporary calf.

Charles Lamb's copy extensively annotated by Coleridge, who says:

24

"to read Donne you must measure *Time*, and discover the *Time* of each word by the sense of Passion." At the end he has written: "I shall die soon, my dear Charles Lamb! And then you will not be vexed that I had bescribbled your book. 2 May, 1816."
Lent by the Yale University Library.

DONNE, JOHN
90 *Poems on Several Occasions*, London, 1719.
Contemporary calf. Keynes 85.
The Jennings–Hayward copy.
Lent by Mr. and Mrs. Robert S. Pirie.

John Donne and The Grolier Club

The revival of scholarly interest in the poetry of John Donne originated on this side of the Atlantic and culminated in the publication by the Grolier Club in 1895 of the first scholarly text, incorporating Lowell's notes in his copy of the 1855 edition and edited by Charles Eliot Norton.

DONNE, JOHN
91 *Poems*, London, 1633.
Contemporary calf. STC 7045, Keynes 78.
James Russell Lowell's copy, given him while he was Ambassador to the Court of St. James, with annotations in red pencil for the Grolier Club edition of 1895.
Lent by William E. Stockhausen, Esq.

DONNE, JOHN
92 *Poems*, London, 1654.
Contemporary calf. Wing D1870, Keynes 83.
This copy was given by Charles Eliot Norton to James Russell Lowell in 1888. It is the only copy recorded with the first quire from the edition of 1649 and a cancel title. All other copies have the reset first quire from the edition of 1650 and a cancel title.
Lent by Mrs. and Mrs. Robert S. Pirie.

DONNE, JOHN

93 *The Poetical Works*, Boston, 1855.
Contemporary cloth. Keynes 89.

James Russell Lowell's copy with notes which formed the basis of the
1895 Grolier edition.
The A. Kingsley Porter copy.
Lent by the Harvard College Library.

DONNE, JOHN

94 Another copy
19th century morocco.

Charles Eliot Norton's copy with numerous notes in his hand for the
Grolier edition of 1895.
Lent by the Harvard College Library.

95 A.L.S. from C. E. Norton to Beverly Chew at the
Grolier Club agreeing to undertake the work of
preparing an edition of Donne's poetry.

As compensation for the editorial work, C. E. Norton requested that he
be presented with Izaak Walton's copy of the 1633 *Poems*, then on the rare
book market. It was paid for by Samuel Putnam Avery and sent to Norton.
Later, Norton received $350.00 as an additional fee, plus six copies of the
book.
Lent by the Grolier Club.

DONNE, JOHN

96 *The Poems*, New York, The Grolier Club, 1895.
Two volumes, cloth gilt. Keynes 92.

The ordinary paper edition of the *Poems*. Of the 380 printed, 375 were
subscribed to before publication. The price was $6.00.
Lent by Mr. and Mrs. Robert S. Pirie.

Brought together for the first time since publication day, 8 November 1895, were the three copies of the Grolier Club edition of the *Poems* printed on vellum.

DONNE, JOHN

97 Another copy

26

Elaborate inlaid morocco.

This copy on vellum was bound by Morrell for Scribners.
Lent by Mr. and Mrs. Robert S. Pirie.

98 Another copy
Blue morocco.

The Club's copy on vellum, bound by The Club Bindery.
Lent by the Grolier Club.

99 Another copy
Elaborate inlaid morocco.

This copy on vellum was bound by the Doves Bindery for an early
owner (probably the first), Fisher Howe of Boston.
Shown also is an a.l.s. to Howe from T. J. Cobden-Sanderson.
Lent by Dr. Gordon Ray.

Musical Settings

FERRABOSCO, ALFONSO
100 *Ayres*, London, 1609.
19th century boards. STC 10827, Keynes 69a.

This volume of Jacobean music, known in only four copies, contains
a musical setting for and two stanzas of Donne's "The Expiration."
Lent by The Newberry Library.

CORKINE, WILLIAM
101 *Ayres, to Sing and Play*, London, 1610.
The Second Book of Ayres, London, 1612.
19th century boards. STC 5768, 5769, Keynes 71.

This early Jacobean song book preserves the music for Shakespeare's
"Whoop, doe me no harm good man" and "To shallow rivers" as well as
Donne's "Breake of Day" and Marlowe's "Come live with me and be my
love." This is the only copy known of the first issue of the first book (three
copies of the second issue are recorded) and one of three recorded copies of
the second.
Lent by Mr. and Mrs. Robert S. Pirie.

Translations

HUYGENS, SIR CONSTANTIJN
102 *Koren-Bloemen*, Graven-Hage, 1658.
Contemporary calf. Keynes 105.

Huygens, described by some as the greatest figure in Dutch literary history, became acquainted with Donne while serving as secretary to a Dutch embassy that was in London in 1622 and 1623. He persisted with his translation of Donne in the face of the remark by Charles I, when he heard of it, that "he did not believe that anyone could acquit himself of that task with credit."
Lent by Mr. and Mrs. Robert S. Pirie.

HUYGENS, SIR CONSTANTIJN
103 *Koren-Bloemen*, Amsterdam, 1672.
Contemporary vellum.

This second edition of the collected poems of Huygens is substantially enlarged and contains translations of Ovid, Ben Jonson, Guarini, and others, as well as of Donne.
The Jennings copy.
Lent by Mr. and Mrs. Robert S. Pirie.

STUBBE, HENRY
104 *Deliciae Poetarum*, Oxford, 1658.
18th century calf. Wing s6040, Keynes 106.

This translation of two short poems of Donne's into Greek appeared in the same year as the much more substantial translation into Dutch by Huygens.
Lent by the Yale University Library.

❀ | MISCELLANY | ❀

Donne's Seals

Other impressions of Donne's "Christ crucified on an anchor" seal are in items 35 and 123, and impressions of his "sheaf of snakes" seal are on items 34 and 37.

DONNE, JOHN

105 "Christ Crucified on an Anchor" seal mounted in gold.

Shortly after he was ordained in 1615, Donne adopted this new seal and not long before he died he gave examples of it to several of his friends, including Izaak Walton. This example was at one time in the possession of Bishop Ken whose half-sister was Walton's second wife. It matches identically the impression in the *Lives* (see items 106 and 123) and probably is the very one given to Walton.

Lent by Salisbury Cathedral Library by permission of the Dean and Chapter.

WALTON, IZAAK

106 *The Lives of Dr. John Donne, Sir Henry Wotton, Mr. Richard Hooker, Mr. George Herbert,* London, 1675. Contemporary calf. Wing w672.

Presentation copy from Walton to his cousin, Mr. Lillie, with a wax impression on page 57 of Donne's seal from the one he gave Walton shortly before he died.

Lent by Mr. and Mrs. Robert S. Pirie.

106a Another copy

See item 123.

GODWIN, THOMAS

107 *Romanae Historiae,* London, 1648. Contemporary calf. Wing G986.

For no apparent reason an impression from another of the rings Donne had made appears on the flyleaf.

Lent by Mr. and Mrs. Robert S. Pirie.

Books Dedicated to John Donne

Copies of these four volumes, being all the books dedicated to Donne, have probably not been together in one place since the dispersal of his library in 1631 (see illustration facing page 17).

TISDALE, ROGER

108 *The Lawyers Philosophy*, London, 1622.
Modern morocco. STC 24090, Keynes 163.

Dedicated to Donne by a friend from his school days about whom little is known save that he apparently held some minor office at St. Paul's and in 1619 was appointed a clerk to the Commissioners for the relief of the poor prisoners in the King's Bench and the Fleet. Only five copies are recorded.
Lent by the Harvard College Library.

ADAMS, THOMAS

109 *The Barren Tree*, London, 1623.
Contemporary calf. STC 106, Keynes 164.

Adams, a preacher of some eminence, whom Southey described as "the prose Shakespeare of Puritan theologians . . . scarcely inferior to Fuller in wit or to Taylor in fancy," dedicated this book to Donne and the Prebend-Residentiaries of St. Paul's whom he describes as his "very good Patrons."
Lent by Sir Geoffrey Keynes.

PETLEY, ELIAS

110 *The Royall Receipt: or, Hezekiahs Physicke*, London, 1623.
19th century one-half calf. STC 19801, Keynes 165.

The delivery of this sermon is the only recorded event in the career of this obscure country clergyman.
Lent by the Massachusetts Historical Society.

DONNE, DANIEL

111 *A Sub-poena From the Star-chamber of Heaven*, London, 1623.
19th century boards. STC 7021, not in Keynes.

Little is known of this cleric who is believed to have been the son of John Donne, Rector of St. Bennet's, but he was not a relative of the Dean's.
Lent by Lincoln Cathedral Library, by permission of the Dean and Chapter.

Books from the Library of John Donne

BARCLAY, WILLIAM
112 *De Regno et Regali Potestate Adversus Buchananum,*
Paris, 1604.
Contemporary vellum. Keynes L16.
From Donne's library with his signature, motto and characteristic pencil markings.
From the Bridgewater Library.
Lent by H. Bradley Martin, Esq.

BLACKWOOD, ADAM
113 *Adversus Georgii Buchanani,* Poitiers, 1581.
Contemporary vellum. Keynes L27.
With Donne's motto and signature on the title page and sporadic pencil markings throughout.
Lent by Mr. and Mrs. Robert S. Pirie.

C., I. D. [i.e. C. de Reboul]
114 *La Cabale des Reformez,* Mompeiller, 1597.
18th century calf. Not in Keynes.
This volume from Donne's library turned up in London in 1967 having been in the collection of the Earl of Pembroke.
Lent by Mr. and Mrs. Robert S. Pirie.

CAMPION, THOMAS
115 *Poemata,* London, 1595.
Modern morocco. STC 4544, Keynes L36.
From Donne's library with his motto and signature, this is one of the few volumes of literary rather than purely theological interest he is known to have possessed.
Lent by the Pierpont Morgan Library.

116 *Codex Canonum Vetus Ecclesiae Romanae*, Paris, 1609.
Contemporary vellum. Not in Keynes.
The most recently discovered book from Donne's library, containing
his signature, motto and some pencil markings.
Lent by B. Weinreb Ltd.

GENTILIS, ALBERICUS
117 *Regales Disputationes Tres*, London, 1605.
18th century calf. STC 11741, Keynes L80.
From Donne's library and later in the collection of Leonard Woolf.
Lent by Dawson's of Pall Mall.

MENGHI, GIROLAMO
118 *Compendio dell'arte Essorcistica*, Venice, 1599–1601.
Contemporary vellum. Not in Keynes.
With Donne's motto and signature.
Lent by John Sparrow, Esq.

PIGGHE, ETIENNE WYNANTE
119 *Annales Magistratum et Provinciarum SPQR.*, Antwerp,
1599.
Contemporary vellum. Keynes L143.
Although Donne's signature and motto have been cut from the title
page, enough of the ascenders and descenders remain to make certain the
identification of this as a book he once owned.
From the Bridgewater Library.
Lent by John Sparrow, Esq.

SERARIO, NICHOLAS
120 *Rabbini, et Herodes*, Mainz, 1607.
Contemporary vellum. Keynes L166.
From Donne's library with his signature, motto and typical pencil
markings throughout.
Lent by H. Bradley Martin, Esq.

Biography

WALTON, IZAAK

121 *The Life of John Donne*, London, 1658.
Modern calf. Wing w668, Keynes 150.

Walton's *Life* first appeared as the preface to the *LXXX Sermons*, London, 1640, but this, the first separate issue, has, according to the author, "fewer blemishes and more ornaments than when 'twas first made publique." This copy has corrections in what appears to be Walton's hand as do at least three other copies, and the remains of what may be a presentation inscription can be seen at the top of the title page.

Lent by Mr. and Mrs. Robert S. Pirie.

WALTON, IZAAK

122 *The Lives of Dr. John Donne, Sir Henry Wotton,*
Mr. Richard Hooker, Mr. George Herbert,
London, 1670.
Contemporary calf. Wing w671, Keynes 61.

Presentation copy from Walton to Henry Hinchman, Bishop of London, with manuscript corrections in Walton's hand. Copies without manuscript corrections by Walton are very scarce.

The Harry B. Smith copy.
Lent by Mr. and Mrs. Robert S. Pirie.

WALTON, IZAAK

123 *The Lives of Dr. John Donne, Sir Henry Wotton,*
Mr. Richard Hooker, Mr. George Herbert,
London, 1675.
Modern calf. Wing w672.

Presentation copy from Walton to Walter Chetwin, the son-in-law of the publisher of the second folio of Shakespeare and nephew of the publisher of the third folio, with an impression in wax from the seal given to Walton by Donne shortly before he died.

The J. C. Lynn copy.
Lent by Mr. and Mrs. Robert S. Pirie.

33

DRUMMOND OF HAWTHORNDEN, WILLIAM
124 *The Works of*, Edinburgh, 1711.
Contemporary calf.
It is interesting that Jonson in these conversations paid more attention to Donne, whom he describes as "the first Poet in the World for some Things," than he did to Shakespeare, who is dismissed in a scant two lines.
Lent by Theodore Yonge, Esq.

Iconography

ANONYMOUS
125 *John Donne.*
Portrait bust. Oil on canvas. Keynes B3.
A late 17th or early 18th century enlarged copy of the 1616 miniature by Isaac Oliver now in the Royal Collection at Windsor. Only four oil portraits of Donne are known, all in England. See frontispiece.
Lent by the National Portrait Gallery, London.

ANONYMOUS
126 *John Donne.*
Contemporary portrait, ca. 1595.
Even in this photograph the quality of this extraordinary portrait, which was left by Donne in his will to his close friend Robert Ker, 1st Earl of Ancrum, is apparent. It disappeared from sight until 1959 when it was re-discovered in the collection of the Marquess of Lothian labelled as a portrait of Duns Scotus.

DONNE, JOHN
127 *Poems*, London, 1635.
Contemporary calf. STC 7046, Keynes D7.
This contains as a frontispiece the portrait bust done in 1591 when Donne was eighteen. It was suggested by Lawrence Binyon that it is based on an original by Hilliard.
Lent by Robert H. Taylor, Esq.

DUGDALE, SIR WILLIAM
128 *The History of St. Paul's Cathedral*, London, 1716.
Contemporary calf. Keynes D12.

On page 62 there is an engraving by Wenceslaus Hollar after the effigy of Donne in St. Paul's Cathedral.
Lent by Mr. and Mrs. Robert S. Pirie.

DONNE, JOHN

129 *Letters to Severall Persons of Honour*, London, 1651.
Contemporary calf. Wing D1864, Keynes D8.

The first edition, with a fine impression of the portrait frontispiece engraved by Lombart after the original in the Deanery at St. Paul's Cathedral.
The Earl of Lonsdale copy.
Lent by Mr. and Mrs. Robert S. Pirie.

TAYLOR, JOHN

130 *Heads of All Fashions*, London, 1642.
Modern morocco. Wing T464. Not in Keynes.

The head in the center of the right-hand side is considered by some observers to represent John Donne. A more convincing case can be made that its counterpart on the left side is William Shakespeare.
Lent by H. Bradley Martin, Esq.

DONNE, JOHN

131 *LXXX Sermons*, London, 1640.
Contemporary black morocco. STC 7038, Keynes D11.

A fine large copy with the rare first state of the portrait before the words "Aetat: 42" were added on the sides of the oval surround.
Lent by the Yale University Library.

BASKIN, LEONARD

132 *John Donne in His Winding Sheet*.
Bronze, 21 inches; cast in 1955. Not in Keynes.
Lent by Mr. and Mrs. Arthur E. Vershbow.

STONE, NICHOLAS

133 *Life-Size Marble Effigy of Donne in His Shroud*.
Carved in 1631. (Full-size photograph, approximate height 10 feet.) Keynes C6.

This remarkable statue was originally within the choir in the south aisle of old St. Paul's Cathedral and is the only monument which survived the Great Fire of 1666 intact.

Shortly before he died Donne caused a wooden urn to be carved, procured a plank the size of his body, and then when charcoal fires had been lighted in his study, he had his shroud put on him, with knots tied at the head and foot. With the shroud turned back to show his face, he stood on the urn while an artist sketched his figure life-size on the wooden plank. This drawing, which he kept by his bedside until he died, served as the design both for this sculpture and for the frontispiece to *Deaths Duell*.

Nicholas Stone, the sculptor, also carved the monument Donne had erected in 1617 in memory of his wife and stillborn child.

Memorial Verses

CAREW, THOMAS

134 *Poems*, ca. 1640.

Contemporary vellum gilt.

This manuscript, containing forty-seven of Carew's poems, is the largest surviving manuscript of his poetry and contains some otherwise unrecorded variants as well as corrections which may be in the poet's hand.

Lent by Mr. and Mrs. Robert S. Pirie.

CAREW, THOMAS

135 *Poems*, London, 1640.

Modern morocco. STC 4620.

The first appearance in print of Carew's elegy on the death of Donne.

The Arbury Library copy.

Lent by H. Bradley Martin, Esq.

CORBET, RICHARD

136 *Certain Elegant Poems*, London, 1647.

Modern morocco, uncut copy. Wing c6270.

This little volume of Corbet's poems, dedicated to Lady Teynham, was apparently edited by John Donne, Jr., and contains Corbet's lovely epitaph on Donne.

Lent by Mr. and Mrs. Robert S. Pirie.

LORD HERBERT OF CHERBURY, EDWARD

137 *Occasional Verses*, London, 1665.

Contemporary morocco. Wing H1508.

Bound in red morocco with the arms of a royal duke, probably those of Charles II as Duke of York, this copy is signed on the title page by the editor Henry Herbert, nephew of the author. It contains Herbert's elegy on the death of John Donne.

The Wilkinson copy.

Lent by Mr. and Mrs. Robert S. Pirie.

KING, HENRY

138 *Poems, Elegies, Paradoxes, and Sonnets*, London, 1657.

Contemporary morocco. Wing K501.

This volume of poems by Donne's close friend and literary executor contains his epitaph on Donne's death which first appeared in the 1633 edition of Donne's poems.

The Britwell copy.

Lent by Robert H. Taylor, Esq.

Modern Editions

DONNE, JOHN

139 *The Poems*, Oxford, 1912.

Original cloth. Keynes 96.

This is the first edition of Herbert J. C. Grierson's great edition.

The Belle da Costa Greene copy.

Lent by Herbert T. F. Cahoon, Esq.

DONNE, JOHN

140 *Complete Poetry and Selected Prose*, New York, 1929.

Original morocco. Keynes 97.

John Hayward edited this volume for the Nonesuch Press. 675 copies were printed.

Lent by Mr. and Mrs. Robert S. Pirie.

DONNE, JOHN

141 *An Anatomy of the World,* Cambridge, 1951.
Quarter morocco. Keynes 77c.

A facsimile of the first edition presented to members of the Roxburghe
Club by Sir Geoffrey Keynes.
Lent by Mr. and Mrs. Robert S. Pirie.

DONNE, JOHN

142 *The Elegies and the Songs and Sonnets,* Oxford, 1965.
Original cloth.

A new edition prepared by Dame Helen Gardner.
Lent by Mr. and Mrs. Robert S. Pirie.

DONNE, JOHN

143 *The Poems,* New York, 1970.
Original boards.

Edited for the Heritage Press by Frank Kermode.
Lent by Mr. and Mrs. Robert S. Pirie.

DONNE, JOHN

144 *Love Poems,* London, 1923.
Orange japanese vellum. Keynes 124.

An "ad imprimandum" copy specially bound and subscribed for by
B. F. Kennett of the first publication of the Nonesuch Press. 1250 copies
were printed.
Lent by Mr. and Mrs. Robert S. Pirie.

DONNE, JOHN

145 *Some Poems and a Devotion,* Norfolk, 1945.
Original boards. Keynes 134.

Lent by Mr. and Mrs. Robert S. Pirie.

NORTON, CHARLES ELIOT

146 *The Text of Donne's Poems,* Boston, 1897.
Original wrappers.

An offprint from Volume V of *Harvard Studies and Notes in Philology and Literature*, presented by Norton to Ferris Greenslet.
Lent by Mr. and Mrs. Robert S. Pirie.

DONNE, JOHN

147 *Paradoxes and Problemes*, London, 1923.

Original boards. Keynes 46b.

Prepared for the Nonesuch Press with a bibliographical preface by Sir Geoffrey Keynes. 645 copies were printed.
Lent by Mr. and Mrs. Robert S. Pirie.

DONNE, JOHN

148 *The Courtier's Library*, London, 1930.

Original green boards. Keynes 127.

Edited by Evelyn Simpson for the Nonesuch Press. 950 copies were printed.
Lent by Mr. and Mrs. Robert S. Pirie.

DONNE, JOHN

149 *X Sermons*, London, 1923.

Original boards. Keynes 33e.

Selected by Sir Geoffrey Keynes for the Nonesuch Press. 725 copies were printed.
Lent by Mr. and Mrs. Robert S. Pirie.

DONNE, JOHN

150 *Sermon of Valediction*, London, 1932.

Original boards. Keynes 33g.

Edited for the Nonesuch Press by Evelyn Simpson. Printed copies numbered 750.
Lent by Mr. and Mrs. Robert S. Pirie.

Bibliography

No 17th century poet has been so well served bibliographically as has John Donne. Three editions of Sir Geoffrey Keynes's bibliography have already appeared and a fourth is in the press.

KEYNES, SIR GEOFFREY

151 *Bibliography of the Works of Dr. John Donne,*
Cambridge, 1914.
Original wrappers.
Three hundred copies were printed for the Baskerville Club and distributed by Bernard Quaritch, Ltd.
Lent by Mr. and Mrs. Robert S. Pirie.

KEYNES, SIR GEOFFREY

152 *A Bibliography of Dr. John Donne,* Cambridge, 1932.
Original cloth.
Three hundred and fifty copies of this second edition were printed.
Lent by Mr. and Mrs. Robert S. Pirie.

KEYNES, SIR GEOFFREY

153 *A Bibliography of Dr. John Donne,* Cambridge, 1958.
Original cloth.
The third edition.
Lent by the Grolier Club.

Memorabilia

F T [F. Terry?]
154 Silver gilt communion cup and paten. London, 1626.
This lovely communion cup and paten were given by Donne in 1626 to the Church at Blunham of which he held the benefice from 1622 until his death.
There is a tradition in the village that when Donne first came to Blun-

ham, he stayed at the Manor and went back to London with a load of cucumbers in his carriage. See illustrations following page 16.

Lent by the Rector and Churchwardens of Blunham Parish Church, Bedfordshire.

ANONYMOUS

155 *Ben Jonson.*

Contemporary portrait.

Jonson was a close friend of Donne's in his younger days and his first appearance in print was a commendatory verse in Jonson's *Volpone* (see item 72).

Lent by the Grolier Club.

FRANCHART, JACQUES

156 *Edward, Lord Herbert of Cherbury.*

Contemporary portrait.

This superb portrait is of one of Donne's closest friends, the man to whom he presented the manuscript of *Biathanatos* (see item 10).

Lent by Dr. Calvin H. Plimpton.

VISSCHER, CORNELIS

157 *View of London, 1616.*

Enlarged photostat showing St. Paul's Cathedral, on the left, of which John Donne was Dean from 1621 until his death in 1631. This entire area of London was destroyed in the Great Fire in 1666.

The Committee on Publications of
the Grolier Club certifies that 500 numbered copies
and 150 additional copies for the compiler
of this catalogue of an exhibition
of the works of John Donne
were printed by
The Stinehour Press in Lunenburg, Vermont,
with illustrations by
The Meriden Gravure Company
of Meriden, Connecticut,
of which this is
copy no.

307